New

Paul Simpton

Illustrated by
David Mostyn

OXFORD
UNIVERSITY PRESS

The trip to Zap was very long.
Nick watched films. He watched
a lot of films.

"Here's a film about your new school," said Mum. She put it on.

"This is Zap School," said the film.

Children from lots of planets come to the school.

5

Jen watched a bit of the film.
Then she went to get a snack.

When Jen got back, she looked at the film and...

"Oh no!" she said.

She ran out fast.
"Stop!" said Nick, but
Jen did not stop.

Nick ran fast. He
jumped onto the pod.
"Stop!" he yelled.

six, five, four, three,

11

"Press the red button!"
yelled Nick.
Jen looked for it, but...

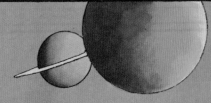

The pod zoomed off!
It was going to zoom into
space *with Nick still on it!*

Jen hit the red button!
The pod stopped just in time.

"Why did you run away?" said Nick.

"There are monsters at the new school," said Jen. "I saw them on the film."

"No!" said Nick. "The monsters are on THIS film! *The Monsters of Planet X!*"